小玻系列翻翻书

小玻的小妹妹

XIAOBO DE XIAO MEIMEI

[英] 艾力克·希尔 著 彭懿 译

接力出版社
Publishing House

小玻，我们要送给你一个惊喜！
Spot, we have a surprise for you!

你有一个小妹妹了！

It's your baby sister!

小玻，我们有一个礼物要送给你。
We have a present for you, Spot.

谁在门口？

Who is at the door?

小玻在给苏茜找玩具。

Spot looks for a toy for Susie.

苏茜把什么拿走了？

What has Susie taken?

苏茜在哪儿呢?
Where's Susie?

小玻，桌子下面是什么？

What's under the table, Spot?

睡一会儿吧，苏茜。
Time for a nap, Susie.

谁在那儿?
Who's there?

小玻，你现在是一个大哥哥了！
You're a big brother now, Spot!

我喜欢苏茜，妈妈。
她太好玩了！
**I like Susie, Mum.
She's fun!**

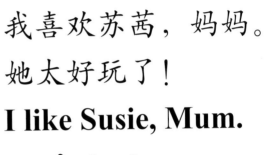

桂图登字：20—2007—120

Published by arrangement with Ventura Publishing Limited, a Penguin company.
Original title:SPOT'S BABY SISTER
Text and illustrations copyright © Eric Hill, 1989
Planned and produced by Ventura Publishing Ltd ,80 Strand,London,WC2 0RL,UK
Eric Hill has asserted his moral rights under the Copyright, Designs and Patents Act 1988.
All rights reserved.

Chinese edition published in 2007 by Jieli Publishing House
The Penguin logo is a registered trademark of Penguin Books Limited

图书在版编目（CIP）数据

小玻的小妹妹：汉英对照/(英)希尔著；彭懿译.—2版.—南宁：接力出版社，
2012.10
　（小玻系列翻翻书：双语故事）
　ISBN 978-7-5448-2662-4

Ⅰ.①小… Ⅱ.①希…②彭… Ⅲ.①儿童文学－图画故事－英国－现代－汉、英
Ⅳ.①I561.85

中国版本图书馆CIP数据核字(2012)第210734号

责任编辑：张培培　　美术编辑：卢　强
责任校对：张　莉　　责任监印：刘　元　　版权联络：王燕超　　媒介主理：高　蓓
社长：黄　俭　　总编辑：白　冰　　出版发行：接力出版社
社址：广西南宁市园湖南路9号　　邮编：530022
电话：010-65546561（发行部）　　传真：010-65545210（发行部）
网址：http://www.jielibj.com　E-mail:jieli@jielibook.com
经销：新华书店

印制：北京尚唐印刷包装有限公司
开本：889毫米×1194毫米　1/24　　印张：1　　字数：10千字
版次：2007年9月第1版　2012年10月第2版　　印次：2016年4月第11次印刷　　印数：88 001—98 000册
定价：15.50元